Doodlebug, Doodlebug Your House Is On Fire!

Doodlebug, Doodlebug Your House Is On Fire!

Stories of the little
curly-headed boy

By James Patterson McRae
Drawings by J.P. McRae

CHAPEL HILL
PRESS, INC.

Dedicated to Mary Lee and her boys
who made my childhood complete.

Contents

Introduction ix

The Little Boy Who Ran 1

The Little Boy Who Liked to Eat 3

The Little Boy Who Climbed 5

The Hayloft 7

The Little Boy's Birthday 10

Springtime 15

The Sliding Board 17

The Fantods 20

The Reed Bend 22

A Hot Day 26

Playing 35

Uncle Jim 37

Dinner at Mary Lee's and More Uncle Jim . . . 43

James McLean and the Nastiest Critter 48

About Going to School 51

Flying 53

Rabbit Hunting 58

Breshin' 62

Peddlin' 65

Camping 71

Introduction

When I was growing up there were no such things as computers, CDs, televisions, or DVDs. Today's children have access to all kinds of electronic toys and gadgets, and they are quite the experts in using them. I, on the other hand, do not know how to use a computer or load a DVD to watch a movie.

Instead of watching adventures, my friends and I created our own. Everything could become a toy: an old worn-out tire, a tobacco stick, or even a June bug on a string. We spent countless hours of running, climbing trees, or jumping around in the hayloft, pretending to be one hero or another.

Times change all the time. I wonder what today's children will remember when they grow old.

I have written about some of my childhood adventures and present them to my family and friends as a gift from the "little curly-headed boy."

The Little Boy Who Ran

Once there was a little curly-headed boy who ran everywhere he went.

He ran across the yard.

He ran through the pastures.

He ran in the bottoms of ditches.

He ran up trees . . . oops!

And up the sides of barns . . . oops!

He ran so fast that he ran across water . . . oops! He ran across water again . . . oops . . . and again . . . oops!

He ran in the rain.

He ran through the snow.

He ran sloshing through the mud.

He ran down the dirt road, kicking up dust.

He ran after calves.

He ran after horses.

He ran after baby pigs.

This little curly-headed boy had a little curly-haired dog named Cotton. Cotton ran everywhere the little boy ran. He would run and run and run. Cotton loved to chase birds. Cotton chased squirrels. Cotton chased cats and baby pigs and rabbits. Cotton loved to run and run and run.

The little boy's father, who was working in the garden, would holler out, "WHY DON'T YOU SLOW DOWN?" as the little boy and his dog, Cotton, ran down the row.

The little boy's mother, who was picking flowers in the yard, would shout out: "WHY DON'T YOU STOP RUNNING EVERYWHERE YOU GO? SLOW DOWN! MY WORD, BOY! SLOW DOWN SOMETIME!"

The old black man, Will, who was going down in the pasture to get the cow for milking time, would mumble to himself, "Run, run, run. Don't you ever get tired of running all the time? Why don't you slow down?"

They just did not understand how much fun it was to run.

The Little Boy Who Liked to Eat

The little curly-headed boy used to climb on top of the grapevine arbor and sit and eat grapes. He climbed up in the apple trees and picked apples and ate them. He climbed way up in the big pear tree to get the biggest and most beautiful golden pears.

He climbed the pecan trees way out on the limbs and shook them up and down to knock down the pecans. He picked up pockets full of nuts and cracked them with his teeth and ate them. His little dog, Cotton, also liked to eat pecans, so the little boy would eat one, and then give one to Cotton.

He would go into the garden and pull carrots, wipe off the dirt on his pants leg, and eat them. The little boy liked to eat really ripe, very red tomatoes that were warm from the sun. He especially liked to eat cherry tomatoes by the handful. He could stuff five or six or seven into his mouth at one time and pretend he was a chipmunk.

He climbed up into persimmon trees to pick persimmons after the frost had sweetened them.

He climbed the grapevines at the edge of the woods to pick wild grapes. Sometimes he would even jump up high to pick wild fox grapes.

He ate wild cherries, wild blackberries, hickory nuts, and anything else he could find.

He ate *all* the time!

The little boy's mother was worried. No matter what she fixed for dinner, her little boy just would not eat. She talked about it to his father, to the neighbors, and to her friends. What could she do? Why did her little boy not want to eat? Why was he never hungry? She did not know what to do!

The Little Boy Who Climbed

The little curly-headed boy loved to climb.

He climbed the pecan trees. He climbed the old cedar tree at the kitchen door. And he climbed the three huge trees that used to line the dirt road at the front gate. But there was no longer a front gate. There was not even a dirt road. The road had been closed back in his grandfather's days. There was grass planted where the road used to be.

The curly-headed boy would sit in the big oak tree on a limb that hung across where the road had been. He would pretend that people and cars and mules and wagons were coming by. Nobody could see him, and he could jump down and scare them, or drop down on the horses' backs and ride off galloping, shouting: "HI-HO SILVER, AWAY!"

But there was no longer a road, so all he could do was imagine. But he could swing on a thick rope that hung from one of the high limbs. He could swing across an imaginary river filled with alligators and crocodiles and all kinds of water monsters. And he could safely land atop one of the low-hanging limbs, out of harm's way.

The curly-headed boy would climb to the very tops of trees where he could sway back and forth in the breeze. Sometimes he could cross over to another tree, high up in the treetops, and come down another tree.

His mother would see him high up in a tree and yell at him, "YOU COME OUT OF THAT TREE, BOY, BEFORE YOU GET HURT!" and she would say to herself, *Why me? Why do I have to have a son who thinks he's a monkey?*

And sometimes his father would see him up in a tree and holler at him, "BOY, YOU COME DOWN OUT OF THAT TREE! ARE YOU TRYING TO SCARE YOUR MOTHER TO DEATH?"

Once, when he was up in the old mulberry tree at the carriage house, the old black woman, Miss Mary Lee, saw him. "BOY, YOU BETTER GIT DOWN OUT'R DAT TREE 'FOR YOU FALLS AN' BREAKS YO NECK!" The little curly-headed boy reached out, grabbed the top of a bamboo growing there, and rode it down to the ground. Mary Lee's eyes got bigger and bigger. She clasped her hands to her mouth and said, "Lawdy, lawdy, Jesus, dat chil', he com' down out'r dat tree lak an angel."

All of the grown folks fussed at the little curly-headed boy about climbing up high in things.

They just didn't understand how much fun it was to climb.

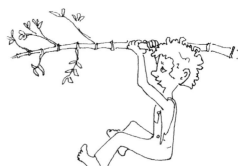

The Hayloft

The curly-headed boy jumped out of bed and tore off his pajamas, leaving them where they dropped and grabbed his bib overalls. One foot in, the other foot in, and down the stairs he went.

"I'm going to have some fun today! Boy, oh boy, the men filled the barn with hay yesterday, and I'm going to climb up to the top of the barn. I'll bet that ol' barn is full!"

He ran out the back door, slamming the screen, and raced toward the barn. The mean ol' rooster flew up in the air at the little boy as he ran past. The hens all half flew, half fluttered away, squawking.

Cotton, the boy's little dog, made a mad dash at the hens, careful to keep away from the rooster. He caught up with the little boy, and they both ran into the barn.

Will, an old black man who was hired to take care of the animals, was the only other soul awake this early. He was milking the cow, ol' Bessie. She was startled when the little boy burst into the milking room and started stomping her feet. Will grabbed the milk bucket and moved it out of the way, then butted the cow in the ribs with his head. "Soo, sook, soo . . . hits jes dat wile young'un . . . soo, sook," said Will to Bessie to calm her down.

He turned to the little curly-headed boy and said, "Boy, wont'cha go somer's widout runnin' sometimes? You 'bout caus' dis ol' gal to step in da pail."

"Sorry, Will. I didn't know you were milking. I'm going to play in the loft." Into the corncrib and up the ladder to the hayloft he went. Cotton decided to hunt some mice in the corncrib.

"Wow, look at this!" the little boy shouted. "I ain't never seen so much hay. It's plumb to the roof! Man, I'm going to have some fun today!"

He found a place where he could climb up to the top of a stack of bales and look around. "Wow!" He climbed over one of the high wind beams of the barn and ducked under another. He climbed the very highest bale of hay, stood up on top of it, gave out a Tarzan yell, jumped across the opening to the hay chute, and landed on another stack of bales.

But . . . the bales of hay buckled when he landed. Backward and head first he went, down through the floor into the empty hay chute. (The hay chute was built wide at the top and narrowed down at the bottom; hay would slide down as the animal ate, until the chute was empty.) And now the little boy was wedged in the hay chute, upside down, right at the floor of the cow stall, and a bale of hay on top of him!

"Oh . . . oh . . . help . . . ugh . . . umph . . . wow . . . somebody . . . help . . . WILL . . . HELP! Ooooh . . . ouch . . . HELP . . . SOMEBODY HELP!"

The little dog, Cotton, came racing around the barn and dashed into the cow stall, barking, snapping his teeth, and biting at the hay chute.

Will came running from the milking room with eyes wide open. He had never heard the little boy cry like this before, and he couldn't imagine what had happened—until he saw the little boy wedged in the chute. He really looked a sight! He had a nail stuck in his right ear, one all the way through his right forearm, and he was bleeding a lot.

Will turned, ran to the woodpile, got an axe, and returned. He cut the hay chute apart, gathered up the little boy, who was moaning and sobbing and scared to death, and carried him to his mama.

Mama took her little darling from Will, piled him in the backseat of the car, and rushed him to the air base hospital. The little curly-headed boy had a deep nail wound behind his right ear and one all the way through his right forearm. He had blood all in his hair and down his neck; hay was stuck to it, and he was covered with black hay dust. The only clean parts of the poor little boy were the two streaks on his face where tears poured down.

He was given a tetanus shot because of the rusty nail wounds, cleaned up, and sent home with "Everything's going to be alright!"

But everything wasn't alright—not by a long shot. Mama's sweet little darling had lockjaw and was paralyzed for two weeks. It was not that he was paralyzed stiff; he was just too weak to move. All he could do was lie in bed and moan. Later, when he was getting better, he could crawl to the bathroom, but most of the time he just lay in bed, helpless.

High fever made the little boy imagine he saw or heard things that weren't really there. He thought there were monsters under his bed, but he was too weak to call for help. He thought he felt bunches of writhing, twisting, and slithering snakes under his pillow, but he was too terrified to look. In his dreams, when he was asleep, he was constantly running as fast as he could, but was never able to outrun a shooting pistol that followed him down the highway.

Finally the little boy got well, but he was still too frightened to look under his pillow. He was scared to put his fingers under the pillow to lift it up. The monsters under the bed were no problem. He had always had them around. All he had to do was to jump into the bed and out of it so the monsters could not grab him by the ankles.

But the very worst thing about all of this was that his mama made him practice piano one hour for each hour he had missed while he was sick. He had fourteen to fifteen hours to make up, and it seemed to take forever to finish them. He hated playing the piano anyway. This was for girls and sissies. He had too many other things to do.

The Little Boy's Birthday

Really early one morning the little curly-headed boy woke up suddenly and thought, *This is my birthday!* He stood up in his bed and jumped as far as he could. He wasn't going to let some ol' monster under the bed grab him by the ankle. He glanced under the bed real quick. No monsters. "Nope, not under there today." (He was almost disappointed.)

Boy, he was really excited about his birthday. He took off his pajamas and grabbed his overalls on the run. Down to Will's cabin he ran. "Wake up, Will, it's my birthday! What ya goin' give me?"

"I'm goin' gib you a bundle of switches iffin you don' stop waking this ol' nigger up 'fore day lak dis. Dats what I'm goin' do, gib you some switches or a piece of black coal. You want some chewing tobacco?"

"Naw, I don't want that old nasty mess, ugh! Come on, Will, get up! We got a lot to do today. I'm going to be four years old today! Get up now, I'll help you milk the cow."

"Don't need no help. All you does is get in da way anyhow. Why'n you go on an' run de cow up from de pasture? I'll be 'long d'reckly."

"Okay, Will, I'll go get ol' Bessie. Hurry up!"

"You watch out for milk snakes, you hear?"

"Okay, Will. Hurry up!"

After the little boy had brought the cow to the barn, Will came and brought him a cold sweet potato for his birthday. They led ol' Bessie into the milking stall, and the little boy fed her some ground-up corn mixed with molasses while Will got the milking pail down from a nail on the wall.

Will finished milking the cow and turned her out. He took the milk to the kitchen to strain it and to put it in the Kelvinator refrigerator. The curly-headed boy went down to Mary Lee's. Miss Mary Lee was an old black woman who sometimes helped his mother.

"Mary Lee, today is my birthday. I'm four years old!"

"Dat ain' ol' boy, wait 'til you is as ol' as I is. Den you'll be ol'."

"What ya goin' give me for my birthday, Mary Lee, huh, what ya got for me?"

"Well, I can't says I has anything in particular fo' you. What does you want?"

"You got anything to eat?"

"What ya mean, does I got anythin' to eat. Course I gots somethin' to eat. You jus' sit yornself down an' I'll sho' you what I gots to eat."

The little boy sat down at the kitchen table, and the old woman started getting him something for his birthday. She poured some Covington Molasses onto a plate and gave him two leftover biscuits. She also fixed him some coffee. She poured some scalding hot coffee into a cup and added a lot of milk and some sugar and stirred it for the little boy. She handed him the cup, and he poured himself a serving into a shallow saucer.

The little curly-head was busy trying to "hem up" his molasses in the plate with a broken biscuit. He was sopping molasses, trying to keep it from running from the biscuit. He lifted up the saucer, blew across it, and sipped some coffee. "Man, this is good," he said as he sipped some more coffee. Pretty soon he had cleaned his plate and had finished his cup of coffee. "Thank you, Mary Lee. That sure was good."

The little boy decided to go by Gusta Farley's house. Gus was a black sharecropper on the land owned by the little boy's daddy. He was already out in the field, dragging land, getting ready to plant corn and cotton, but Magnolia, his wife, was there.

"Hello, Miss Magnolia, how are you today?"

"I is jus' fine, Mr. Jimmy, how you doin'?"

"Oh man! I'm fine, Miss Mag. Today is my birthday. I'm four years old today!"

"Well, ain't that jus' gran'. You wants a chicken leg? I got sum I jus' took outa d' spider an' it's still hot. Wants one?"

"Yes, ma'm. Thank you, ma'm, that sure would be nice," answered the little boy. He took the piece of chicken and said good-bye. "I think I'll go find Gus, Miss Mag. Thank you for the chicken."

Dats a nice little man, thought the great big black woman, as the little boy disappeared around the barn, heading for the field.

When the little boy got to the field, Gus was at the far end, turning the mules around. Gus looked so small to the boy, and he wondered why things got smaller and smaller when they got farther away. He didn't want to wait for Gus, so he waved at him and walked back home to see his mama.

"Good morning, Mama, how are you?"

"I'm fine, Darling. Come here you little early bird." She hugged him and ran her fingers through his hair, trying to smooth the curls.

"Will told me that you waked him up before day. Why don't you just stay in bed like sensible folks?"

"Oh, Mama, I'm too excited to stay in bed! Mama, I'm four years old today! Mary Lee gave me some coffee; I blew on it in a saucer, Mama, just like Mary Lee does."

"That's fine, Darling, but don't you think you're too young to drink coffee?"

"I'm four years old, Mama; anyway, Mary Lee put a lot of milk in it. It was good, Mama!"

The little curly-headed boy was happy, but for some reason he was sad, too, and his mama could feel this. She was determined to find out what was wrong.

"Want something to eat, sugar? Are you hungry?"

"No, Mama, Will and Mary Lee and Miss Mag have already given me something. I ate some of Gus's breakfast chicken. Don't you think that's funny, Mama, eating fried chicken for breakfast?"

"No, Baby. Gus doesn't like to eat early. He gets out his mules and goes to the field every morning at first light, and he'd rather wait for something to eat. Miss Magnolia sends him fried chicken and biscuits and ice water every morning about 9:00 o'clock. By that time he needs something really good to eat."

"Anyway, Mama, I'm not hungry. We going to have birthday cake today?"

"We sure are, and some ice cream, but we have to wait for your sister to get home from school."

"I'm not ever going to school, Mama!"

"Why not, Baby?"

"'Cause Will didn't go to school, and he can do anything. Gus didn't go, and James McLean didn't go but two days, one in the first grade and one day in the second grade. Mama, I don't need to go to school. I already know a lot of things."

"We'll see," said his mama.

The little boy started looking a little bit sad again, and his mama just right out asked him, "What's wrong, Baby? You don't look happy, and you're supposed to be happy. It's your birthday!"

"Mama," he started to cry. "Mama, yesterday I was three years old and I thought I'd be bigger today, but I'm not. I'm just the same size. It's not fair. Four-year-old boys are supposed to be big and strong, and I'm just like I used to be," and he continued to sob pitifully.

Mama sat down and pulled her curly-headed boy to her and hugged and kissed him on his salty cheeks. "Now, now, sugar, don't you fret your little head. You are big enough just like you are. One of these days you will be so big that you'll have to duck to walk under the sky. And you're going to be ugly. Why, you're going to have snaggle teeth and a long nose, and only one eye, and you'll have hair growing all over your back."

"Aw, Mama, that's not true. I'm alright now, Mama." He hugged her and ran out the kitchen door, slamming the screen. He picked up a stick and started chasing that ol' mean red rooster.

Springtime

❦

It was a beautiful spring morning. The little boy was sitting under the chinaberry tree, just watching what was going on and petting his little dog, Cotton. The trees were putting on new green leaves, the grass was growing green again, and the sky was bright blue.

Martins had returned and were busy building nests in Gus's martin gourds. They flew back and forth from around the yard to the gourds, carrying dried grass, old pieces of baling twine, and small tufts of cotton from the mule barn to their nests.

Gus and Ted, his oldest son, were already in the field, turning ground with mules and bottom plows, going around and around the large fields, seemingly taking forever. The little boy watched some chickens scratching on the ground, picking up bugs and worms.

Soon it would be time to plant corn. During the winter the best ears of corn were selected to shell for seed. He remembered the time he had joined a large group of friends and neighbors who had come together for a corn shelling at the corncrib. The large round kernels at the butt end of the ear and the small round kernels at the tip were first shelled off for the chickens. Only the kernels from the middle of the ears were shelled off for seed, because these kernels were all the same shape and size and could be planted easily. It didn't take long before the little boy had a giant blister on his palms, because his hands were not quite as tough as those of the men. While all the shelling was going on, Cotton had been busy sniffing out mice and catching some of them.

Miss Mag, Gus's wife, was heating water at the woodpile in the wash pot, getting ready to do the week's washing. When the water was hot enough she shaved off slices from the homemade lye soap into the water and stirred it with a paddle into a sudsy froth.

She put in the white clothes and sheets first and stirred them in the now boiling water. Then she pulled them out with the paddle and dumped them into rinse water. Darker and dirtier clothes followed next to be boiled clean.

Miss Mag rinsed and wrung the clothes out by hand, again and again, and then hung them out on a line, or spread some of them over hedge bushes.

Miss Mag got her basket and headed to the corncrib where young poke salad was beginning to show. The young poke-berry bushes were growing around the base of a clay hill where the old mule barn used to be. This was on the little boy's way home, so he gathered himself up and fol-lowed along with Miss Mag. Every year in spring, people from all over the farm would go there to gather new spring greens.

Miss Mag was glad to see the new poke salad. She knew that it would taste really good and that it would be good for her family. Hard freezes in December and January had burned all of the turnips and collards. It had been awhile since any of them had eaten greens; they had mostly eaten fatback, biscuits and molasses, and chicken and rice. Miss Mag knew her family was ready for some greens.

The Sliding Board

❦

The little boy awoke to a beautiful spring morning. The birds were calling in the first light of day, and the little boy could not wait to get going. He grabbed his overalls off the chair with one hand while he tugged off his pajamas with the other. Skipping and jumping on one leg he dressed as he raced toward the stairs. No one was awake, but he was sure that his mama would be awake soon. He knew that she did not miss anything and that the slightest noise would awaken her.

He stumbled through the back hall and headed for the kitchen on a dead run, skidding and sliding on the wood floors. Out the back door he flew, jumping all of the steps to the ground. The screen door slammed behind him.

The little boy's dog, Cotton, came scrambling out from under the porch steps, barking and with his tail wagging. They ran toward the barn, with Cotton jumping up at the boy while they ran. They cut through the dogwood trees, scaring out the chickens that roosted there every night. Cotton chased the old rooster until he flew up at him; he dodged the rooster and fell in behind the little boy. They tore around the big pine tree and ran to the barn, into the corncrib, just past the milking room.

The little boy knew there was a long, really wide board blocking off the ear-corn from the passageway, and he had big plans for that board. The day before his mama had taken him to play with some of the town kids at the Presbyterian church playground, and he had been astonished about all the different things to play on. He tried everything—the swings, the seesaws, and ran around the ball diamond. He even climbed up on top of the log hut, climbing up the log ends at one corner and then pulling himself up on the roof. Everything was fun, but the best thing to the little curly-headed boy was the sliding board. He climbed it and slid down every which way, again and again. He really had fun. And then the little boy remembered the old long board in the corncrib and thought, *Well, now, I believe I'm going to make me one of them things.*

He pried at the board, but it was nailed to two posts and would not come loose. He climbed up into the loft, got a pitchfork, and used it to pry at the board, trying to pull the nails loose, but it did not work.

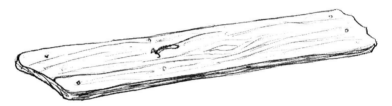

The little boy looked around to see what else he might use but could not see anything else inside the barn. He walked back outside and looked under the wagon shelter for something. He spied an old brickbat and figured that it might just do the job. After digging it out of the dirt with his fingers, he ran back into the barn.

Using the piece of brick like a hammer, he pounded on the board until it came loose. After beating the nails down flat with the brick, he grabbed up the board and got it out of the barn somehow. He struggled with the big old, long board, dragging it across the yard to one of the huge elm trees, where he succeeded in propping it up into the fork of a limb.

He got it sloped just right and then climbed up the back side of the tree, just using his fingers and toes gripping in the scaly bark of the big old tree. He settled into the crotch of the limb and got ready.

"All right now, man-o-man-o-man! I got me a sliding board, just like the city boys! Boy oh boy, here I go!" The little curly-headed boy sat down on the board, put his feet first and slid down. "Yipee Yi . . . Yow . . . Ow . . . Help . . . Mama . . . Help . . . Somebody come help me!"

The little curly-headed boy had gotten his hind part stuck on one of the bent-over nails sticking up through the board. He could not slide down, and he could not climb back up. All he could do was scream for help and cry.

Finally the little boy's mama heard him screaming and came running. "What have you done now, boy? What've you got into now?" When she saw him hanging halfway down on the board, she realized he was too high up and knew she had to get some help to get the little boy down. She ran back to the house for help. Mr. Will was bringing up the cow for milking, and she hollered for him to come and help.

Both the little boy's mama and Mr. Will lifted up the board with the little stuck boy, got it off the tree and put it flat on the ground. The little boy was screaming and hollering, tears were running down his cheeks, and he was sobbing and gasping for breath. They had to slide him back up the board to get him off the nail, with him screaming even louder.

Later that morning, after his mama had gotten him cleaned up a bit and he had calmed down and quit crying, she took him to town to the doctor's office for a tetanus shot, so that he would not get lockjaw from that old rusty nail.

The little boy never did make another sliding board. The next time he would slide down anything it was a real sliding board on the school playground when he was in the first grade. He never did tell anybody about his homemade sliding board.

The Fantods

The little curly-headed boy felt bad; he felt crummy. He felt so bad it was almost like when somebody says something cruel and hurts your feelings. But his feelings weren't hurt, he just felt bad. He was not sick; that morning his mama had felt his forehead and didn't have a fever or anything.

He did not think he had a cold, but come to think of it . . . he did cough a little . . . ah huh . . . ah huh . . . and his eyes were red and burning and his nose was running. He wiped his nose on his sleeve.

He just did not feel good at all. It was spring, and the men were planting corn. The trees were leafing out, and flowers were in bloom; it was warm, and birds were singing everywhere. It was the kind of weather when a little boy should be having fun roaming and exploring, but he just did not feel good. He felt as if he was in slow motion. When he walked it felt like his legs were hard to move, and his feet sure did feel heavy.

The little boy had walked out to the field where Gus was planting corn. He sat down on a stump at the end of the row.

When Gus made his round he saw the sad-looking little boy sitting with his head in his hands.

"Boy, wha's ailing you?"

"Hmmph!"

"Wha's da madder, da cat got your tong?"

"Naw, Gus, I feel like my behind is dragging. I don't feel good at all."

"Boy, looks lak you gots de fantods, tha's what."

"What's de fantods, Gus?"

"De fantods is when you feels lak you does. Das when you thinks you can do som'thin' but you can't. It's lak de vapors. It's lak you jes don' hav' de get-up to get up and go."

"Well, Gus, I reckon' I got de fantods then, 'cause I's sure don't have no get-up-and-go. I reckon' I'll just go home."

Miss Mary Lee saw the little boy coming to the house with his head hung low, shuffling his feet in the sand. She cocked her head to one side and said: "Lil' Bo-Peep, you looks lak som'body done took your play-pretty. Wha's da madder wid you, boy?"

"Gus says I got de fantods, Miss Mary Lee. I just don't feel good. My feet are draggin'."

"Boy, don' sound lak you gots de fantods to me, sound lak you got da can't-hep-its. Do it seem lak you can't hep it?"

"Sure does, Miss Mary Lee. I want to feel good and I try to feel good, but seems like I just can't help feeling bad."

The little boy's mama came into the kitchen and asked her boy if he felt any better.

"No, Mama, I got de fantods or de can't-hep-its, and I sure feel kind o' low."

"Fantods or can't-hep-its? Can't-hep-its, my foot, you don't have the can't-hep-its. All that's the matter with you, sugar, is spring fever."

The little boy dropped his head down into his hands and sighed, saying to himself, *It don't seem like to me it matters what you call it, I still feel bad.*

The Reed Bend

Mary Lee's boys — there were seven of them — and the little-curly-headed boy were best friends. There was Ol' Dad, Chile Baby, Lacy, Lorenzo, Jerry, Jerome, and Rabbit. They did almost everything together. They tromped through the swamps, jumping from tussock to tussock. They rolled old car tires all over the farm. They had mock battles and chinaberry fights, but the very best, the most fun thing that they did, was to swing from top to top of bamboos in the Reed Bend.

The little curly-headed boy had been to town with his mama. He was getting big enough to ride in the front of the car, but he liked the backseat the best. In the back he could stand up on the floor and drape his arms over the front seat; he was taller that way and could see more. In the front he could not see over the dashboard, and he could not stand up because his mama made him sit back down in the seat.

Anyway, they were finally home from shopping. His mama had stopped to talk to some of her friends, and it had taken most of the afternoon. The little boy had been bored in town and was very tired and listless. He sat down on the front steps, with his elbows on his knees and his head in his hands. His dog, Cotton, came and sat beside him.

"I want something, I want . . . but I don't know what I want," he said to himself. "Maybe I'll go bust a watermelon — no, it's too hot — I'll get one in the morning when it's cool. Maybe I'll go in the house and get a glass of ice tea," but he did not get up. "Maybe . . ." The little boy lay back on the cool floorboards of the porch and closed his eyes. Cotton came closer and snuggled up beside him; he patted his little dog and rubbed his fingers through Cotton's curly fur.

Both of them were almost asleep when the little boy suddenly perked up. He thought he had heard something. There it was again! "Whee-a-whee-a-wheeeee!" His eyes opened wide. He bolted off the porch and started running. "Whee-a-whee!"

It was one of Mary Lee's boys calling him. "Come on, let's go to the Reed Bend and ride some bamboos!" The little boy answered, "Wheee-a-wheet! Be right there!"

They raced each other to the Reed Bend to an old mulberry tree, deep in the bamboos, which was their meeting place.

Chile Baby was the first one there. He was already up in the tree when the others got there. The tree was quite easy to climb, because the old big trunk was leaning over a little bit and had knurls and knobs and broken limb stumps sticking out everywhere. They scampered up to the top of the tree.

They sat in the top of the tree for a while, just talking. Cotton busied himself by hunting mice and rats in the underbrush.

"How you doin', Bo Peep?" they asked the little boy.

"Doing fine; how y'all?"

"We's okay. You goin' to the movie Satu'day?"

"Naw, Mama won't give me any money. She says I been bad."

"What difference dat make? Yo' always bad! She got plenty money."

"Might be," the little boy answered, "but she ain't going giv' me none of it."

"Let's see who can ride the furthes'."

Since Chile had won the race and had climbed the tree first, he got first turn. He launched himself out of the big ol' tree, grabbed a limber bamboo top, and started riding hand-over-hand from one bamboo top to another. After that, each boy grabbed a reed and started their journey across the tops of the bamboos. Each would go in any chosen direction out toward the edge of the Reed Bend, traveling hundreds of feet.

Chile was already climbing the tree again before Lacy and Lorenzo (everybody called him Lo) had made it to the outer edge. Lo was the youngest boy there and always the slowest. He didn't weigh enough to make the bamboos bend much, so his ride was slower than the other boys'. As each boy got to the edge, the last bamboo would take him out into the open space and down to the ground. They continued doing this all afternoon, taking a different direction each time.

Soon it was getting dark, and the boys heard Mary Lee calling them to supper. Mary Lee's boys took off running; they wouldn't dare not to answer their mama's call. It didn't matter at all to Mary Lee whether they had heard her when she called. If they did not come fast, they would get a beating.

The little boy and Cotton ran home, too. It was almost getting dark, and it would be time for supper.

The curly-headed boy burst through the kitchen door, slamming the screen. His mama lowered her head and looked him over through the tops of her eyes. "Boy, you get yourself in the tub and wash some of that filth off if you want to eat with the rest of us!"

"Aw, Ma, do I have to?" knowing all along what the answer would be. He headed toward the stairs.

"And put on some clean clothes! I'm getting tired of those same old dirty overalls!"

"Aw, Ma," he said, climbing the stairs.

"And you wash those dirty ears, you hear? You've been down in the Reed Bend, haven't you?"

It always amazed the little boy that his mama always knew where he had been that day by the type of dirt she saw in his ears.

A Hot Day

❧

It had been hot all night, and it seemed to the little boy that he had not slept at all. His hair, his pillow, and the sheet were wet from sweat. He decided he might as well get up even though it was still dark.

"Sure do hope Daddy takes us swimming today. It's already hot, and it ain't even daylight." He got dressed and ambled down the stairs. He went out the back door, letting the screen door slam shut. His little dog, Cotton, came out from under the steps, stretching each leg, one at a time.

"Maybe Will's up." The red rooster and the hens were still roosting in the dogwood tree next to the barn. The little boy could hear ol' Maude, the big draft horse, stumping her big feet and swishing mosquitoes with her tail.

The wet grass felt good on his bare feet; it was almost cold. He didn't understand about dew and why most mornings the grass was wet. He walked on down to Will's old log cabin and was glad to see the flicker of a kerosene lamp inside. He knew that Will was already up and cooking something.

"Morning, Will! How are you today?"

"Fine, boy. You up purty early. Wha's da madder, can't sleep?"

"That's right, Will. I stayed in the bed just as long as I could. You hot sleeping, too?"

"Yassa, shore were. It's too blame hot fer any soul to sleep in dis heat. Shore hope hit goin' rain today. Seem lak when it gets dis hot and dry, purty soon hit going to rain. When you sees dem whirl win's going 'cross de cotton patch, alifting dem wilty leaves and pickin' up dus' when hit cross de road, purty soon hit goin' rain."

"I sure do hope so, Will. Seems like there's dirt everywhere. Hope Daddy takes us swimming today."

"Boy, you ain't asceer'd o' snakes in dat creek where you swims?" asked Will.

"Naw, ain't never seen one at the swimming hole, but I seen a big ol' water moccasin down at the trestle yesterday. Aunt Rene killed it with her bait hoe. That thing was 'most as big as my leg! Rene broke the handle of her hoe, she chopped at it so hard! Jim will have to make her another."

"You boys always a-playin' under dat trestle on dem big stones. I shore does hope don' none of you git snake bit under der! Looks like to me you could fin' some better place to play."

"We're goin' take some of them big rocks and dam up the creek someday and make us a pond where we can take boats and such back in the woods."

"Don' you s'pose dat de railroad mens goin stop you boys from dat? Come a big rain and de railroad bridge get washed out when yo' dam bust."

"You reckon', Will? You don't reckon' that it'll rain that much, do you?"

"Why shore, hit'll rain 'nuf to bus' a little boy's dam. You ain't seed no rain yet. Back in '29, or '27 it were, all dese fiels here was under water. Folks 'roun' here 'bout starv' to deff. Peoples had to eat fish cranes and seagulls and such. Boy, you ain't seed no rain lak hit can rain!"

"No, I guess I ain't." said the little boy. "Sure do hope it rains some today, though, to get rid of some of this heat. What you cooking in that spider, Will?"

"Jes' some hoe cake; goin' to fry up some salt-cured possum strips in a bit. You wants to eat some?"

"Sure! Ain't never eat no possum; ain't it real fat?"

"Jes' lak hog bacon, boy. Der is a streak o' lean in de fat, taste almost lak bacon. Gimme a han' an' draw us some water, den we be ready to eat."

The little boy and the old man sat down on the porch bench and ate their hoe cake and possum. Will drank his water out of a tin coffee cup, and the little curly-headed boy drank out of a grape jelly jar.

After the two had finished the repast, Will set the tin plates on the porch for Cotton to lick clean, then wiped them off with his sleeve and put them back in the cupboard. "Well, I guess I'll go get ol' sook cow and git my day started."

"Thank you, Will. 'Preciate the breakfast. The possum was pretty good."

The little boy didn't know where to go or what to do next when Will went to the barn to milk ol' Bessie. He started walking down the ditch bank beside the field road, looking for anything at all. He spied a maypop vine growing on the far side of the ditch. It looked like one of the fruits was turning yellow.

He thought, *Man, those things are good. Let's see if I can cross over.* He looked up and down the ditch, searching for a good place to cross over. Finding none, he started to cross anyway, briars and all.

"Ohh . . . ah . . . oh my . . . turn loose, Mr. Briar . . . aw . . . ouch . . . darn-a-mighty . . . wow, these briars hurt!" About that time he stepped on a piece of broken green glass and cut his foot.

"Aw, man, that's goin' to take awhile to heal! Darn-a-mighty!" He put the glass in his pocket.

He grabbed a root growing out of the far bank to pull himself up and gave a shove. The root pulled loose along with a big chunk of bank, and instead of climbing up, down into the bottom of the ditch he went with dirt cascading all around him. The little boy shook dirt out of his hair, blinked his eyes, and tried again. He made it up the bank on the far side and found his maypop. "Man, that thing's not ripe; it's just a yellow leaf. Dad blame it! Here I go and got hurt for nothin'!"

The little curly-head stumbled out through the maypop vine, but got tangled up in some old rusty barbed wire somebody had thrown on the ditch bank. "Dad blame it; I done cut my ankle now; Mama is going to beat me for sure."

He thought he heard a rabbit and started creeping along the ditch bank to see if he could get a look, but he never saw anything. *It's probably just Cotton down in the ditch trying to get a rat,* he thought.

Next he went by the old airplane hangar to see what was in there. Cotton was sniffing under some straw, jumping straight up in the air and then pouncing on something. He came out with a mouse, shaking it wildly. Cotton killed the mouse and then started off hunting some more, pouncing at little noises under the old straw.

The dirt floor under the shelter was pure dust. The boy got a straw and started stirring it around in the dust around some cone-shaped holes, singing, "Doodle bug, doodle bug, your house is on fire; doodle bug, doodle bug, come out of your lair." Pretty soon an insect with big pinchers crawled out of the dust to see what was disturbing his house. "Hello Mr. Doodle Bug, your house is not on fire. It's just me, and I'm a liar."

The little boy went by the corncrib to see if there were any bats asleep in the loft. He did not see any bats, but he found a good snake skin draped over an old discarded bushel basket. He put the snake skin and a red-wing blackbird feather into his pocket.

He went outside and over to the hole in the ground that had been a deep-water well. There used to be an old mule barn, but it had been torn down years ago. The well had been used to draw water for the mules. The men on the farm had been trying to fill up the old well hole with rocks and other things, but were unsuccessful. No matter what was thrown into the well, it would disappear, so nobody believed that the well could ever be filled up.

The little boy leaned over the hole to see if he could still see water. "Yep, water is still there; ain't nobody going to fill up this hole."

He went on down the hill to the big mulberry tree in the Reed Bend. He didn't want to ride bamboos today, so he just climbed up the big tree and sat awhile. Cotton was hunting in the underbrush as usual. "Man, it's still morning, and it's so hot you can hardly stand it. I'm going to find me some place that's cool. Sure do hope Daddy takes us swimming after dinner."

The little boy could not think of any place that would be cool, and he did not know what to do. "Believe I'll go home and see if Mama has any ice tea. Yeah, that'll be good. Come on, Cotton, let's go!" He whistled for his little dog and slid down a big bamboo growing beside the big tree.

The two of them started toward the house across the cotton fields. The little boy was too short legged to stride across the rows; he had to jump from row to row, dodging between the cotton stalks. The closer to the house he got, the taller the cotton was. It really grew well in the clay up the hill.

Suddenly, he felt something burning like fire on his neck; he slapped and clawed at his neck and shoulder. "Ow . . . ouch . . . ooh . . . oh, oh, oh, oh . . . what the devil is stinging me?"

He swatted at his neck, and some kind of wooly worm fell off to the ground. "Dad blame it, man alive, that hurts! Ain't puttin' that thing in my pocket!"

He wanted to take the caterpillar home to show to his mama. His neck was still burning like crazy from the sting. The little boy picked up two twigs and tried to pick up the wooly worm with them, but it kept rolling off, falling to the ground. He got flustered and finally ground the wooly worm into the dirt with the heel of his bare foot. "That'll fix you, Mr. Wooly Worm! You won't set nobody else on fire!"

When he got to the house, his mama was preparing dinner. They almost always had tomato sandwiches and a sliced cucumber to eat this time of year, because his mama said it was just too hot to cook.

"Mama, can I have some ice tea?"

"Sure, baby. What's wrong with your neck? It is really red. Something sting you?"

"Yeah, Mama, some ol' yellow wooly worm. I stomped it to death."

"And your ankle and foot, my Lord! Boy, you've been bleeding. What'd you do this time? You're not going to grow up to be a man. You're going to kill yourself for sure! Why don't you be careful sometimes? How'd you do that?"

"Mama, I stepped on some broke glass; here, I got it in my pocket. And I got this here snake skin and a red-wing blackbird feather. Ain't it pretty?"

"Boy, you get that nasty ol' snake skin out of my kitchen! Throw it out the back door!"

"Aw, Mama!"

"'Mama,' nothing. You do as I say, or I'll pop you one!"

"Aw, Mama." He went to the door and threw his three treasures out. "Don't do no good to find things if I can't keep nothing," he mumbled to himself.

"Here, boy, here's your tea. You wash your hands and face and sit down a while."

"Okay, Mama."

After he had finished the tea he asked his mama, "You reckon' we goin' to go swimming today?"

"You'll have to ask your daddy about that. I know I'm not going. Too many of those biting flies at the creek to suit me."

"Okay, Mama, I'm going to find Daddy. Bye." He ran out the back door, letting the screen door slam shut.

"Tell your daddy that dinner's about ready, to come on in!" His mama shook her head slowly from side to side. "That boy, he won't ever shut the door easy."

The little boy pretty well knew that his daddy would be in the garden, pulling weeds or something. He and his little dog, Cotton, ran toward the garden. Sure enough, his daddy was there, bare-backed, bending over and pulling weeds.

Pow! He slapped his daddy on his hot, sunburned back, as he was running by him, hollering, "Howdy, partner!" To his great amazement, he received a swift kick in the seat of his pants, lifting him up off the ground like a football and propelling him down the row.

The little boy picked himself up and glared at his daddy. "What'd you do that for, kicking me like that?" He put his hands on his hips and declared, "When I'm a grown man and have a little boy, I'm going to be nice to him."

His daddy answered, "Boy, don't you be running by people and slapping them on their hot back. You about scared me to death! I hope I didn't hurt you, but I didn't even think, you surprised me so bad."

"No, I ain't hurt. I'm sorry, I was jus' playing."

"Didn't feel like playing to me."

"Mama said to come on in, dinner's about ready. Can we go swimming this afternoon?"

"I don't see why not, it's too hot to work. I am about burned up anyway. My back feels like burnt toast, especially since you buttered it so well," answered his daddy with a wink, tousling the boy's hair.

"Sorry, Daddy. I didn't think."

His daddy picked up his shirt at the end of the row, put it on, and they walked to the house together.

After dinner, everybody went out to the screen porch, the coolest place in the house, to rest a while. This was a time to talk, to relax, and to rest. Even the little boy, who most of the time was running around somewhere, liked to rest after dinner. His older sister, Robin, seemed to like to rest all the time. She had learned to read quite well and liked to lie on her bed upstairs, reading.

The little boy did not know how to read yet, but if it meant that you had to lie around all the time, he avowed that he didn't need to read. There was way too much to do to lie around and read all the time.

He heard his daddy telling his mama, "They closed the swimming hole up at X-Way mill pond last week. Seems like the health department has been testing the creeks around here and found out that the water is contaminated. They found out that Morgan Mills is dumping sewage and fabric dye into Gum Swamp, and it's contaminating the water downstream."

"That's bad," remarked his mama. "Everybody likes to swim in the race at X-Way. The water seems clear enough."

"Yes, but evidently it is not clean. They think that people will get sick if they swim in the water."

The little boy was listening to his parents and thought that this was foolish. The water at X-Way was swift and cold as ice and seemed just right to him. He often would go fishing with his uncle at X-Way in the race below the dam. His uncle always caught plenty of robin and bream there. He just could not believe that the water was bad.

"You know the place we go swimming is about eight miles below X-Way on the same creek. I wonder if it's contaminated also."

"I sure hope not. That's the only place we have to go swimming since the air base closed off the Lumber River to swimming."

The little boy hoped they were not going to close his swimming hole. He loved to jump into the water out of the tall cypress tree, just like the older boys. And it did not matter that he could not swim yet because he sure was trying hard. He had no problem staying up in the swift current or paddling over to the bank. But every time he tried to actually swim and lift his legs up, he would go right under. The swimming hole was shallow enough that he could reach the bottom, so the little boy pretended to be swimming by walking on the bottom and moving his arms. He thought it looked like he was swimming, but he really was not.

When they got to the swimming hole at the end of the Country Club Road, there was nobody around. A yellow sign nailed to big cypress tree read:

DANGER! THIS WATER UNFIT FOR SWIMMING.
AREA CLOSED BY ORDER OF SCOTLAND
COUNTY DEPARTMENT OF PUBLIC HEALTH.

The whole family was disappointed. It truly was hot and everybody had been looking forward to a refreshing dip in the creek, *But no!*

Author's Note: It was two years before they could go swimming again. World War II was over, and the Laurinburg-Maxton air base was closed. While the air base was still open, the access to the swimming hole at the river was fenced off. Now the Lumber River was open again to the public. The army had made some improvements at the swimming hole. There were two diving boards, one low and a high one, and someone had tied   a thick rope high up in an overhanging tree. Boys could carry the rope end with them and climb up another tree, hold on to the rope, and swing very far out, high above the water, and then drop off into the water.

There were stories about two soldiers who had broken their necks and had drowned by diving out of the tall trees, but the older boys still tried it. Luckily no one ever got hurt.

The water was black and very cold. It had a swift current and it was hard to swim upstream, but it was worth the effort, because floating back downstream to the swimming hole was great.

Playing

The little curly-headed boy and his best friends, Miss Mary Lee's boys, loved to play just about anything they could think of.

They rolled old car tires for miles and miles and miles.

They pretended to be old Chevrolets and cranked and putt-putted and scratched off sand and dust with their bare feet and swerved their bodies and came to screeching stops.

They played dog and ran around on all fours, kicking up dust and barking.

They played Tarzan and rode bamboo tops across the Reed Bend. They swung on long grapevines across deep ditches and bottomless pits, filled with old green water and full of snakes.

They challenged each other all the time. They raced to see who was the fastest, who could throw the farthest, who could climb the highest, and who could eat dry biscuits the fastest without choking to death.

They peeled back the bark of tall okra stalks, broke the woody center part out, and played "Daddy," whipping each other with the okra whop. "Boy, you better cry!" they'd say, copying what their daddy would tell them. *Whip, whip, cry, whip, whip.* "Hush! What are you crying for?" *Whip, whip, whip.* "Boy, you better cry! Shet up that infernal fuss! Cry . . . shet up . . . cry . . . Boy, you'd better hush . . . ," and on and on. Occasionally, one of the

boys would get whipped so bad that he would be whopped right over the fence into the calf pasture. Right back through the fence he came to be whipped some more.

They played horse with old tobacco sticks, riding them astraddle. They whipped their legs with long switches to make themselves run faster and faster. They kicked up their heels and whinnied and jumped ditches and low fences and ran and ran and ran.

They played war with chinaberry balls—"chiney balls"—choosing sides, and then shying balls underhanded at each others' heads.

They played and played and ran and ran and then played some more.

Uncle Jim

∾

The little boy found his old worn-out automobile tire in the bushes and headed down to Mary Lee's house rolling it. The tire was off somebody's jalopy and was worn so thin that it felt soft to the little boy's hand. It was bald all the way around and almost worn through in places, but it was a good, lightweight, lightning-fast roller.

He ran along, rolling his tire down the rut in the road. It would stay in the hard rut a long time. He could always run a few strides before he had to pat it again, propelling it faster down the road in front of him.

Mary Lee's boys saw him coming, grabbed their tires, and met him at the barn. They all headed straight past the barn down the long road leading to Jim Ingram's house. "Maybe we can get Uncle Jim to tell us a tale." Uncle Jim Ingram was the brother of Mary Lee's husband, and he loved to tell stories.

Jim was at the woodpile, splitting some biscuit wood for one of the girls. Coot and Annie Bee, Uncle Jim's daughters, were both good cooks. Miss Rene, Jim's wife, with her big self, was sitting on the porch while one of the girls did the cooking. Coot could make the very best, most mouthwatering biscuits you ever tasted. They were even good cold.

Uncle Jim had an old dog, Red, with a split nose. Seems like he sniffed at the chopping block a little too close one time too many when Uncle Jim was splitting wood. He could not smell a rabbit in front of him but he could sniff out one really well to either side.

"How you boys today? How you, Mr. Jimmy? How you brother-boys?"

"We fine, Uncle Jim. Hope you doin' alright."

"Yassa, couldn't be betters. Don' know as I felt dis good in a long time." Jim put down his axe, gathered up the split pieces of wood, and took them into the house.

The boys sat down on the porch steps to wait for Uncle Jim to return, hoping he would tell one of his stories.

"Aunt Rene, you been fishin' lately?" one of them asked.

"Law no, Chile, hits too hot and de water 'bout dried up. Ain't nothin' but dem lil' two-finger bluegills a-bitin' now. All dey does is eat yo worms, ain't wurf it."

"Yeah, Aunt Rene, shore is dry alright. You seed any snakes lately?"

"Las' time I be at de trussel I kilt a big ol' cottonmouth. He was a-laying in de shade right under the railroad bridge, right side dat lil' footpath what goes down de bank."

"What ya say, Aunt Rene, tha's right where we likes to play on dem big ol' rocks."

"Das right, boy, right der where you all plays. You boys goin' git snakebit iffn you don' watch it."

"How come you ain't asceer'd o' snakes, Aunt Rene?"

"Sceer'd, why I be sceer'd? I gots eyes, ain't I? Cause I don' go a-floun-derin' in places where I can't see. I ain't like you foolish boys, I looks where I goes. Ain't no no-shoulders goin' strike dus ol' gal, no siree. But y'all now, y'all goin' git et by one o' dem big ol' cottonmoufs 'cause you in so much a hurry you can't take time to use dem eyes what God give you. Yassa, one o' dese days one o' dem big ol' snakes goin' eat one o' y'all."

"Sure hope not, Aunt Rene."

About that time Uncle Jim came back out on the porch and sat back in one of the straight-back chairs, leaning it against the side of the house.

"What ya' boys doin' rollin' dem ol' tars? I don' see how you has fun roll'n dem ol' things all over creation. In my days, we didn't have such truck, weren't no rubber tars then. We had to roll ol' arn wagon rims 'round. Weren't no fun, 'special when one o' dem big heavy rims fell on yo' foot an' 'bout breaks it."

Uncle Jim reared back in his chair, recollecting back to the good old days.

"What we children loved to do were to grab us a 'bacco stick and ride it strad'l lik' a hors'. We'd git switches and whup our sticks and whinny lik' a hors' an' kick up our heels and run 'roun' in circles and had us de bes' fun. Had me a stick called 'Ol' Paint,' could outrun any 'bacco stick hors' 'roun'. Boys giv' all der sticks horse names."

"We play da same, Uncle Jim. It's fun."

"Speak'n o' hors's, had me a white hors' one time. Pretties' hors' you ever seed, weren't no work hors', no sirree, were' a rid'n hors'. I us'd ride dat fine stallion ever'wher'. Hit weren't like ridin' a ol' mule, a clunky-clunk. Hit were like a-ridin' on a cloud, he were so smoof. Dat hors' he look lak his foots not touch de groun', he pranc'n so fas'. An' set'n up on his back jes da same as float'n. Yessa, dat white hors' he were de bes'."

Uncle Jim paused to spit a stream of tobacco juice.

"He were de fas'es' hors' 'roun' dese parts, weren't no hors' 'roun' ever cou'd keep up wid him. Dat hors', he look lak he lay'n down a-goin' to sleep he run so fas'. He be stretch' out so long when he run, he look lak he be fly'n thru de air. God knows dis ain't no lie, dat hors' he were de bes'."

"Uncle Jim, dat de truf? Is you tell'n us da truf? You ain't never had no white ridin' horse, is you?"

The chair came down noisily, and the feet of the chair slammed down on the porch floor. Uncle Jim sat up straight at the front edge of his chair, pretending to be angry.

"Shor' I hav' a ridin' hors'! You boys thinks I ain't tellin' de truf? Where you come off sayin' I ain't tellin' de truf? God knows I's tellin' de truf, dat ain't no lie. You boys better mind your moufs, you ast me is I tellin' de truf, hmm. Don' mind yo' mouf, I show you de truf on de end of a stick!"

"Uncle Jim, tell us 'bout the year it rain so much, de year water were runnin' up de hill."

"Tell you nothin', you don' mind yo' mouf. Dun tol' you 'bout dat rainy year before, ain't goin' tell you no more. You ast is I tellin' de truf, hmm."

"Please, Uncle Jim, we forgets what you said 'bout de rain. Tell us again, we won't ast you no more."

Uncle Jim started mumbling to himself, just loud enough so the boys could hear him.

"Hmm, ain't tellin' de truf, who does dey think I is? Dey think I's some kind o' fool what goes 'roun' a-tellin' lies? God knows I won't tell no lie. I'm goin' git me a strop an' whup ever one o' dem boys up to an' includin' dat li'l white-headed boy o' Mr. Jimmy's, das what I'm goin' to do. I'm liable to whup ever' one of 'em, call me not tellin' da truf."

The boys could hear every word and sat there really quiet, acting as if they were scared of Uncle Jim. Aunt Rene was snickering behind her hand the whole time Jim and the boys were all fooling with one another.

"Tell us 'bout de rain, Uncle Jim, an' we won't ast you no more. Please, Uncle Jim, we'll be good. We believe what you say, we know that you're tellin' de truf."

"Okay now, boys, you list'n good 'cause dis is da las' time I be tellin' dis tale. God knows I ain't lie'n. Hit rain so much in '29, or somewhere along in dere, dat all dese fiel's 'roun' here were und'r water. Der weren't no crops a-growin' an' der weren't noth'n hardly to eat 'bout dese parts. Water be so high in de fiel's dat water run out of de ditch's into de road. Water so high en dese parts hit run up dat clay hill yonder. Yea, God knows, I ain't tellin' no lie, der were fish cranes and seagulls al 'bout dese parts. People didn't have nothin' but turnips to eat, didn't have no cornbread, didn't have no biscuits!"

This reminded Uncle Jim of the biscuits his daughter was baking. He hollered, "Coot, ain't dem biscuits ready yet? I'm hungry! Hurry up wid dem biscuits!"

Uncle Jim continued telling his story.

"Anyhow, der weren't hardly nothin' to eat in dese parts, 'cept'n dem fish cranes an' gulls. Weren't for dem fish cranes, all us be starv' to deff. Hit rain so much dat one day, I tie de mule to da corner o' da house, right der, an' went in da house to get me sumpt'n to eat, and when I come out, der weren't nothin' but da mule's ears a-sticking up out of da groun'. I had to take a shov'l an' ditch de water off so da mule could breef. Yassa, God knows I ain't lie'n, hit really rain in '29."

"Uncle Jim, da mule sink down in dat hard groun' right der? Seem like it too hard fer a mule to sink in de groun'."

"What is you tellin' me, dat I ain't tellin' you de truf? Dat you don't b'lieve dat da mule sink down in de yard right der?"

"No, no, Uncle Jim, we know dat you is tellin' de truf, but it do seem like da groun' mighty hard der."

"Tell you boys what you needs to do. You needs to get your lil' bony be-himes up off my steps an' git on back to you' own houses. I'm goin' to tell your daddies dat you show dis ol' man disrespe't an' God knows, I ain't tell'n no lie. Y'all git, you hear, y'all git on home!"

"Okay, okay, Uncle Jim, we believe you. We know dat you is tellin' de truf, but dat yard shore looks mighty hard to be swoller'd up no mule."

"Y'all get on away from here! I'm goin' to tell your daddies on ever' one of you."

Aunt Rene was laughing outright by now. She told the boys to come back next week to hear some more lies. Uncle Jim had already gotten up and had gone in the house to eat some fresh-baked biscuits with wild plum jelly.

"Y'all come back now!" called out Aunt Rene, as the boys rolled their old car tires down the dirt road, laughing.

"Ridin' a white horse look like he lays down goin' to sleep, he run so fast. Shucks, Uncle Jim ain't ride nuthin', he shy back out of de way when de mule switch his tail. Shoot, Uncle Jim ain't never rid a billy goat, much less no white racehorse."

One of the other boys continued, doubting Uncle Jim's truthfulness.

"Yea, and water ain't run uphill, don' make no differ'nce how much it rain! Mule sink down at de corner o' de house! Dat groun' so hard a army tank won't sink down. Anyways, where'd Uncle Jim ditch de water to if'n it high as he say? If it high as de top o' dis here clay hill den wouldn't be nothin' but Uncle Jim's ears sticking out o' de groun'. Water'd be plum over the top of Uncle Jim's house!"

They all were laughing. The boys always felt good after hearing Uncle Jim's tales. "Let's go back to Uncle Jim's next Sunday!"

Dinner at Mary Lee's
and More Uncle Jim

One early afternoon, the little boy went down to Mary Lee's house. The whole family was sitting at the table, eating Sunday dinner.

"Boy, you done et? You wants to come set wid us?"

"Yes'm, Miss Mary Lee. I already had dinner. Mama fixed us some tomato sandwiches."

"Tomato sandwiches! Boy, you starve to def eat'n dat truck. You come on an' set down wid us. We got stew chicken an' rice an' fresh garden peas wid pastry, biscuits wid plenty o' butter, an' grape Kool-Aid. Atter dat, I cooked up dis here poun' cake."

"Yes'm. Thank you, ma'm. I believe I'll taste just a lil' bit."

The little boy sat down with Ralph, Mary Lee's husband, and the boys to a fine Sunday dinner. Mary Lee, Mary, and Eula Bee served the table.

A large round serving tray with a mountain of biscuits was placed on the table. Ralph reached out smoothly and lifted the top biscuits and then the little boy's hand darted to the tray.

"Bet ya I can eat a biscuit fast'r'n you can!" he said, challenging the other boys.

Ralph Ingram took his time buttering his biscuit, while the boys were about to choke to death, eating theirs dry.

Mary placed the pitcher of Kool-Aid on the table in time to save the boys. The little curly-headed boy sure was glad to drink some of the Kool-Aid.

Things settled down, and everybody enjoyed filling up with the good meal. The best was the cake after the meal was finished.

The little boy got up from the table and walked into the kitchen. "Thank you, Miss Mary Lee. I'm about to bust I'm so full. It sure was good. How come y'all eat so late anyhow? My mama feeds us 'bout noon."

"Honey, it's Sunday. Don't nobody work on Sunday, so all dey gets is two meals. What you jes et were dinner an' supper. Won't nobody get mor'an cold biscuits atter dis."

"Well, it sure was good. Thank you." The little boy went out the back door. Chile Baby and Lacy were already in the yard throwing some China balls at the chickens. Lacy was a sure shot; every time he aimed at one, a pullet did a two-step. All the boys were just rambling around trying to see what they could throw at. Chile Baby tried again and again to hit a flying bumblebee.

"Man, you can't hit no bumblebee. You crazy?" Everybody laughed.

Lacy shied an underhand shot and knocked the bee right out of the sky.

"Wow, you see dat! Lacy done knock' dat ol' bumbley bee clear out o' de sky. Dats a good one." Everybody agreed that was something.

"I seen one o' dem paper hornets' nest las' Sadderday a-hangin' on a lil' ol' wile cherry tree. Bet you won't chunk no Chiney ball at dat thing."

"Come on, les go fin' it." The boys climbed over an old, rusty hog wire fence and forced their way through some briars and sumac bushes.

They found out it was an old empty hornets' nest after bombarding it with China berries and dirt clods. Finding it empty was a disappointment, and everyone quickly lost interest. "Who cares 'bout an ol' hornets' nest?" Lorenzo knocked it down with a long sapling.

They were halfway down to Uncle Jim Ingram's house. Somebody suggested they go by and see Uncle Jim.

Jim was sitting on his porch, shaping some hickory handles. There were long curlicues and shavings all around Jim's chair on the floor.

"Howdy, boys, what you boys up to?"

"Oh, we jes sashay'n 'roun', ain't doin' nothin'. What ya mak'n, Uncle Jim?"

"Oh jes some ol' hoe handl's. Jes set'n here an' scrap'n dese long curls off'n de stick wid an ol' piece o' broke windo' glass, das all."

"You goin' scrape dat saplin' down to a hoe handl' wid dat glass, Uncle Jim?"

"Sure is, don' take long. I ain't doin' nothin' no way, dis here is jes rest'n."

"Uncle Jim, we jes come out o' de mulberry orchard and walked right pas' de place where dey used to snake out dem big ol' cypress trees. Tell us 'bout da deep ol' hole down der in de swamps."

"What? Tell you what? Why I goin' tel you 'bout a hole? All you boys do is laff behin' my back and snigger 'neath yo han's. Tell you nothin', das what I goin' do. Tell yo daddies, das what I goin' do! Sure! Tell yo daddies don't none o' you 'spect nothin'. Everyone o' you boys needs a whupping, das what!"

"Naw, Uncle Jim, we'll be good. Tell us de tale 'bout dat hole down in the swamp."

"Hole? Ain't no hole, hit's a pit, das what! Hole gots a bott'm, das what; dis here ain't got no bott'm, hit's a bott'mless pit."

"What you mean, Uncle Jim, ain't got no bott'm? Hit go clean to China?"

"Das it, ain't tell you nothin'. Don't belieb nothin'. Don't belieb nobody. You boys jes wants to be disputatious. You boys ought to be 'shame, disputin' ev'ry soun' I makes. My own brofer's boys too! Little Mr. Jimmy, I doesn't blame you lak I does dese brofers boys, I knows dat you jes tag'n 'long wid dem. Don' make no sense dat yo daddy 'low you to truck wid dese here ruffians."

"Uncle Jim, they ain't bad. All us boys love to come down here an' listen to your stories. You tell a real good story; tell us 'bout that ol' bottomless pit."

"Aw'right, I tells you, but you brofer boys you jes hush, don' wants to hear nothin' out o' ere one o' you. You hear me now?"

"Yessa, Uncle Jim, we be 'spectful."

"Aw'right, now you'll jes set der an' don' say nothin'. You does dat, we be aw'right."

"Aw'right, Uncle Jim." The boys settled down on the porch floor and let their legs dangle off the side of the porch.

"Right 'bout where dat ol' wile cherry tree wid de broke-down lim's sets, you know da one where you boys clim' to get at dem wile grapes a-growin' up in it, right 'bout der is where we mens used to pull out dem jack cypress. We have bull oxes an' big ol' draff horses an' we hitch 'em to the butt-end of a cut-down cypress and pull dat tree up de hill where hit be buck'd into fence postes. We throw'd a couple o' big cypress 'crost dat deep hole to skid de trees 'crost an' we always careful to not fall in."

Uncle Jim leaned back in his chair and continued with his story. "Come one Sunday, jes lak today, my white ridin' horse come up missin'. I looks all over creation for dat ol' horse, but never did find him. Onliest thing I fount were de foot prints agoin' into dat hole.

"Well, I ponder'd over dat an' I figur'd. Didn't seem lak to me dat lil' ol' hole were deep 'nough to swallo' no full-grow'd horse."

One of the boys asked, "What you do, Uncle Jim? What you do?"

"Boys, you jes hush, and' I tells you." Uncle Jim rolled his eyes at the boys and got back to his story. "I took an' cut me one of them long thin saplin' trees an' got to pok'n down in dathole an' hit swallo' dat saplin'. I took two long saplin' an' lash dem end to end an' stuck dat down in dat hole, an' hit swallow bof poles.

"Dat were 'nough fer me, I left dat place. You boys mout oughta be careful when you's playin' down in de swamp. You be careful cross'n over dat hole what ain't got no bott'm."

"Uncle Jim, we likes to play down der. Hit sure is cool down in da swamp. Ain't no yellow flies nor 'skeeters down der."

"Der is snakes, boy, an' dem big ol' teranchula spiders. I seen one had caut hisself a sparro' an' he set'n back, eat'n dat li'l bird lak somebody set'n at de table."

"Uncle Jim, we don' never see no cott'nmoufs down in de swamp an' we goes everwher'. We walks 'crost dem cypress knees and jumps from tussoc' to tussoc'. We go way back up in der."

"You ain't seed no cott'nmoufs don't mean der ain't none. You see a ol' black lim' a-layin' on de bank or som'tn look lak de root o' a tree, ain't no lim', hits liable to be a snake. You look again an' dat ol' black lim' or dat root ain't der no more. You boys scare off de snakes wid yo hollerin' and laffin' an' such."

"You be right quiet like and ease thru der an' you see plenty o' cott'nmoufs and water-rattlers, too. Plenty! Don't knows why you boys ain't been et by one o' dem big ol' snakes."

"Uncle Jim, you been all down in da swamp, ain't you?"

"Sure, I been all acrost it. Der's a island en de main run o' Ropers, where Black Branch joins up; nice lil' piece o' lan' plenty big 'nough to set on an' cook up what fish you catch in der. Plenty o' fish en der too. People catches 'em all out der at de railroad trussel, but ain't hardly nobody fishes up en da run. You boys ever seed dat island?"

"No, Uncle Jim, de water gets too deep an' we can't go dat far."

"Speak'n o' deep water, I ever tell you boys 'bout de time . . ."

"What, Uncle Jim, 'bout what time?"

"Boys, didn't I hear Miss Mary Lee a-callin' you? Ain't it 'bout time to get yo chores?"

"It ain't dat late, Uncle Jim, but if Mama call'd, we'd bett'r go. She'll whup us fo sure if she call us an' we don' come a-runnin'. See you, Uncle Jim!"

Jim laughed to himself. "Ain't no Mary Lee call'd dem boys, jes want'd to see if'n dey'd run! Dey'll be back nex' Sunday to hear 'nother story."

James McLean and
the Nastiest Critter

Mary Lee's boys and the curly-headed boy rolled their car tires down the long farm road; some places hard and easy to roll on, others impossible. There were places in the road where the wagon wheels had cut down deep into the sand; they were even hard to walk on. The boys had to roll their bald car tires with both hands and hold them up while rolling them, or carry them across the deep sand pockets.

They wanted to get to a patch of wild plum bushes near Joe Sam's (James McLean's) house. These plums were different from those near the

boys' house. They were bigger and sweeter; they were yellow plums, whereas all of the others on the farm were small red ones.

"Man, these are good plums—ain't a sour one in the whol' patch; dose plums down in front of Gus's house'll lock your jaws!"

"Yeah, but Miss Mag sure can make some mighty fine plum jelly out of them. Mama says you need sour plums to make good jelly," said the little curly head.

The boys had their pockets full and their cheeks puffed out with plums. "Le's go see Joe Sam." They went up the path a short distance to James McLean's. The boys called him Joe Sam, but not to his face.

At about the same time that the boys arrived at Joe Sam's yard, he came stumbling down the back steps of his house. He had been drinking all week and was feeling kind of bad. He was a little unstable, rocking back and forth.

"How you boys today?"

"Fine, Mr. James, how you?"

"Poorly, boys, purty poorly, uhm. Seem like I can't stand in one place." He was still rocking back and forth. "Why'nt one of you boys go and feed my mules for me?"

"Okay, Mr. James." Chile Baby and Lacy rushed to the barn to feed up for Joe Sam. All the boys all liked him; it didn't matter at all that he was drunk.

Mr. James McLean and the other boys walked out to the mule lot. James McLean had an electric water pump and had water piped all the way to the barn. One of the boys turned on the spigot, and water started running in the water trough.

Mr. James had the REA run electricity to his house and had installed his own water well and pump. He knew how to do just about everything. Nobody else in the community knew anything about putting down a well, but Mr. James did. In addition to being a good farmer, he was a good auto mechanic, a good carpenter, and even had his own blacksmith shop.

Mr. James was getting old. His wife had passed on, and all of his children had moved to town. He couldn't walk as well as he used to, so he bought himself an old two-mule riding plow. This allowed him to get twice as much work done in the same length of time.

When they all had finished watering and feeding hay to the mules, they went back to Joe Sam's house. He sat down on the side of the front porch and looked at the boys who were standing around. "You boys know what the nastiest critter around is?"

"No, sir, we sure don't, what you reckon it is?"

"Well, what do you reckon a cat eats?"

"Cats eat rats."

"Yep, dey does. What do you reckon a rat eats? Rats eat peas and corn and cheese."

"Sure do," the boys said.

"And what do you reckon a chicken eats?"

"Well," said the boys, "chicken'll eat anythin'."

"Thas right," said James McLean. "Chicken eat peas and corn, but he'll also eat that ol' rat if he's dead and'll eat rat turds, too. Chicken spy that ol' cat diggin' a hole in the sand to go to the bafroom in, cat back up to the hole and get set shakin' his tail a little, chicken standing behind a bush wid his head cock'd to one side, jes a-wait'n for that cat to cut one. Chicken'll catch it every time before it hit de groun'."

The boys could not believe their ears. "Ugh, wish'd you hadn't told us that! We goin' eat fried chicken tonight for supper. Man, I wish'd I hadn't heard dat."

The little curly-headed boy said, "Well, we got to go now, Mr. James. We see you later."

"Okay, boys, you 'member 'bout dat ol' chicken now, you hear!"

"Ugh, come on, le's go. Man, I wish'd I hadn't heard dat!"

The boys headed back home, but they had lost some of their spirit somehow. None of them wanted to race their old tires, so they just rolled them along, kind of slow.

About Going to School

∽

"Mama, I ain't going to school!" declared the little curly-headed boy. "Will didn't go to school and neither did James McLean, and both of them can do just about anything. Robin don't like school; she's crying every day when she gets home, and it don't make sense that a person has to do something that makes them cry!"

"I know, Baby. It doesn't seem right, does it? Your sister hasn't been to school but one week. She'll soon love it, and you'll like it, too, when you get old enough to go."

"I don't know, Mama. Robin says all they let 'em do is sit in chairs. She says they won't let them talk, and they make them put their heads down and sleep all the time. Don't sound much like I'll like it to me."

"Child, they are going to learn all kinds of things—how to read books and to write and to do arithmetic and play games and color pictures and have plays where they pretend they are princes and princesses and things as such."

"I don't want to be no prince, or no king, or color no pictures, and I can already read what the ol' hen scratched in the dirt. I don't care if I can't ever write; what do I need to write for? Will can't write, and he can do anything. James McLean can't read or write, and he can build a barn, or a house, and can fix any ol' car there is. Why do I need to read or write? Reading

51

ain't going tell you when the ol' mule is sick, or when the cow is off feed, or when the ol' hen is ready to set. Seems like to me, there's plenty to read right here without reading books."

"I know, Honey, and you're smart to know about reading the signs of nature. You'll need to be able to read all kinds of signs in life, but you also are going to need to be able to read books and to write down on paper all of the thoughts that you have in your head. You are going to be glad that you can count, add up money and subtract, and do all kinds of other things with math. Who knows, maybe one day you will be building things, even bigger and better than James McLean."

"Aw, Mama, you make it sound alright and it ain't alright! I don't want to go to school and sit in a chair all day. Mama, I'll go crazy! Ain't there some other way to learn, other than sitting all the time?"

"You'll see, you'll learn to like it. Now hush, I don't want to hear any more about not going to school! You go play; go on outside and play with your dog or something. I got work to get done."

"Okay, Mama. I still ain't going to go to school, though."

"Hush about that and go outside. I got to finish these clothes. Go, play!"

"Okay, Mama, but I ain't goin . . ."

"Hush now! Go on before I whip you!"

"Okay, Mama."

The little curly-headed boy walked slowly out the back door letting the back door slam. He called his little dog, Cotton: "Come on, Cotton, let's go kill some rats!"

Flying

❦

Howie Wank and his wife, Betty, lived in the little boy's house during the war. Howie was an army pilot, based at the Laurinburg-Maxton air base. There was an off-base housing shortage due to many new people coming to work at the air base. The little boy's parents decided to help by offering room and board.

Laurinburg Air Base was a glider pilot training facility. Howie flew big paratroop carriers and pulled gliders. Lightweight wood and cloth glider planes were pulled close to the enemy lines by other planes, and then turned loose. Because they had no motor and were as silent as the wind, they could sneak up on enemy territory at night. Every day, the sky was full of airplanes that looked like model planes from the ground.

The little boy woke up one morning and started his usual rambling. He and Cotton had already been at Will's cabin and had helped him fetch the old milk cow down in the pasture. As they continued their rambling, the little boy saw something big and shiny through the sassafras trees on other side of the ditch bank. He knew something was not right. The little boy and Cotton ran over to cross the ditch on a foot bridge that was built over the deepest part of the ditch, right where the very old, wild peach tree had blown down. One could pick ripe peaches from the foot bridge and use the tree limbs as handrails when going across.

The two of them crossed over, and lo and behold, there in the cotton field was a glider plane that had crash landed! The little boy ran to the plane, jumping across each cotton row. There was a man with the plane.

The little boy was sure that this was an enemy pilot — probably a German.

But it was not an enemy. It was just one of the air base gliders that had not caught the right wind and could not make it back to the base. The pilot made friends with the little boy and let him climb in the glider and sit in the pilot's seat. The plane was built really simple. Later, when the little boy was building model airplanes out of balsa wood and paper, they looked like they were made just about the same way the glider looked.

He asked the pilot if he was hungry, and finding out that he was, he raced back to his house. His mama fixed the man some breakfast. The little boy returned to the glider with a full plate of biscuits and jelly, grits and ham and scrambled eggs. He even brought a jug of coffee for the man.

The pilot asked the little boy to come back that afternoon at 2 o'clock to see something surprising. He had contacted the base on his walkie-talkie; they planned to retrieve the glider that afternoon.

While waiting on the plane, the pilot set up two tall poles with a rope between them, far in front of the glider. There was another rope coming down to the ground and back to the nose of the glider, where it was hooked.

The little boy did not need to return at 2 o'clock, because he never left the glider pilot's side. He asked him a thousand questions: "Why are you putting the two poles in the ground? Why'd you tie a clothesline between them? What kind of rope is this anyway? How they going get you back in the air? How do you talk on that walkie-talkie? You ever shot any Germans? You ever been shot at?" And on, and on, and on . . .

He really had never seen rope like that; it was not like the cotton plow lines that he knew about, and it was not like that sticky old brown rope. It reminded him of the silk thread his mama had, just that this was much bigger. It was a new kind of rope, called nylon; he had never heard of it before.

In the afternoon, a little before 2 o'clock, the pilot made the little boy go stand on the ditch bank, out of the way. An airplane flew over the cotton field; the glider pilot talked to it on his walkie-talkie, got into the glider, and closed the door.

The airplane made a long, slow turnaround and flew way down low, close to the ground, having a long rope hanging down behind it. Something on the end of the long rope hooked on to the clothesline; the rope attached to the glider got really tight, and then the glider was lifted off the ground. The airplane pulling the glider climbed higher and higher, and they headed back to the air base.

The little boy was excited. He still could not believe what he had just seen. He did not know what was going to happen. It sure looked like the airplane was flying quite fast when it hooked the rope and jerked the glider up into the air.

That evening, he told his mama and Howie Wank about the glider. Howie said that they rescued gliders all the time. When the little boy's mama left the kitchen, Howie whispered, "If you won't tell your mama, I'll take you up in one of those big airplanes tomorrow!"

"I promise I won't tell nobody!" whispered the little boy, excitedly.

"Good then, I'll come get you tomorrow after dinner and I'll sneak you on one of those paratroop carriers."

Man, oh man, the little boy thought. *I'm going to fly in an airplane, wow! I ain't goin' tell nobody about this; I sure don't want Mama to know.* He was much too excited to sleep that night, and he had to wait all the way to dinner time the next day until Howie came back.

Howie told his mama that he was going to take the little boy for a ride out to the air base to show him the airplanes.

When they got there, Howie took the little boy to one of the airplanes. It was painted in a brown army color on the outside; there were no seats anywhere on the inside, except where the pilot sat. Benches, going down each side wall, were for the paratroopers to sit on. The little boy had seen plenty of airplanes up in the sky, but he couldn't believe that they were this big. He did not understand why those airplanes in the sky looked silver; the one he was in certainly was not silver.

The big airplane took off from the airfield, and the curly-headed little boy looked all around everywhere. Everything on the ground was getting smaller and smaller. Howie called him and told him to look down at the ground. "What do you see?" he asked.

"Nothing but a little ol' doghouse with boxwoods growing around it," answered the little boy.

Howie laughed. "Those aren't boxwoods, they are trees. That little doghouse you're looking at is your daddy's big house. We're way up in the sky, and things look little from up here. If you were down at your house looking up at us right now, this airplane would look just like a silver toy airplane."

"Wow, that's my house down there? Dad blame, it sure is tiny; it looks like a doll house."

Later, on their way back home from the airfield, they drove right by the prisoner of war camp. "Howie, why do those men have these big P.O.W. letters on the back of their shirts?"

"Boy, those men are prisoners of war. They are German soldiers who were shot down and sent over here."

"Germans? They ain't Germans. There ain't nothing German about them! They're just walking around inside that fence like anybody else. You must be kidding me—those men can't be Germans!"

"Yes, they are, too; every one of them got shot down over France, was captured and sent over here."

This just did not seem right to the little boy. He had heard people in town talking about Germans, and how they were supposed to be mean monsters. They were "Krauts"; Krauts were those trolls that hid under bridges and grabbed you by the ankle when you tried to cross the river. Those men inside that barbwire fence sure did not look like some Krauts to him. They looked just like anybody in town, and they sure did not look dangerous.

Seems like, thought the little boy, *everything out here at this air base 'pears to be something it ain't. Trees look like boxwoods, houses look like dog houses, and Krauts look like regular people in town.*

"I just don't know nothin'," he said to himself, as he slouched back in the seat.

Rabbit Hunting

ॐ

The little boy could hardly believe his ears when Gus said to him: "Okay, boy, you meet me at first day tomorrow an' we'll go rabbit hunt'n. You thinks you can clim' out o' your bed in time to meet me?"

"Oh boy, oh boy! We goin' hunting, Gus? You ain't never allowed me to go before now. Sure, I can get out o' the bed. I'll be ready before you!"

It was just dusk and the little curly-headed boy hurried home to get ready to go to bed so he could get up early. "Boy-oh-boy, I'm going hunting rabbits with Mr. Gus!"

He got home and told his mama that he was going to take a bath early so he could be ready to go to bed.

"Lord, Son, what's wrong? Are you sick? What's the matter, Baby, you feel bad?"

"Naw, Mama. Mr. Gus is going to take me *rabbit hunting* in the morning! *Me*, Mama, I'm going rabbit hunting! I got to get up real early so I can meet Mr. Gus at first day. I better go take my bath and go to bed."

"Hold up a minute there! You can't just run off like that—tell me more! What do you mean go rabbit hunting? Nobody has any shotgun shells; this is war time, and the army has all the gunpowder. How're you goin' to shoot rabbits without shotgun shells? And Gus doesn't have any dogs; how're you going to catch any rabbits? And aren't you mighty little to be going hunting anyway?"

"I don't know, Mama, but Gus told me we were going hunting, and I got to be ready! Gus, he'll figure out someth'n."

The little boy bathed and got in the bed. All he could think about was hunting, but pretty soon he fell asleep. It seemed like he had not slept at all when his mama was shaking him gently to wake him up the next morning.

"Get up, Baby, it'll soon be the light of first day and you need to get dressed and eat something. I've got some biscuits and molasses and a glass of good cold milk ready for you right now. Hurry up and come on down and get something to eat!"

"Okay, Mama. Thanks for waking me. I thought that I could get up by myself, but I sure was sleeping good."

The little boy tore off his pajamas; put on his overalls, a flannel shirt, socks, and brogans; grabbed his jacket and was on his way to the kitchen.

Mama had a fire going, and the big room was nice and warm. The little boy sat down at the enamel-top kitchen table and started sopping molasses and drinking his milk. After he was finished, he ran to the back door. "See you, Mama. We'll be back soon."

The little boy's mother was not worried at all about him; she knew that Gus Fairly would take good care of her little darling. It seemed like Gus nearly loved the little boy as much as she did. *It's a wonder,* she was thinking, *that a black man with a houseful of his own children takes up so much time with a little curly-headed white boy. I guess that ol' Gus can tell just how much that sweet little boy loves him. Oh, well.*

Gus was sitting on his porch drinking a cup of really hot coffee, right off the wood stove. It was so strong it smelled like three cups of coffee to the little boy.

"Morning, Gus, how're you this morning?"

"Well, lookie there, would you! I thought that I'd have to wake you up. Your mama must've woke you up, I know you didn't get up by yourself.

Want some breakfast? Mag, bring this boy some biscuit and side-meat and cool him down some of that coffee with milk."

"Naw, Gus, I done ate. I had some biscuits and molasses and milk already. I don't need more."

"Shucks, boy, you can eat some side-meat. Hurry up, Mag!"

Gus's wife, Magnolia, brought the little boy a big cup of creamy looking "coffee" and some side-meat sandwiched in biscuits.

"How you, Miss Mag? Thank you for the breakfast. I'll eat it all."

"How you this fine morning, Mr. Jimmy? Say, you all going hunting, eh?"

"Yes, ma'm. Gus goin' take me with him."

"Boy's goin' be my dog. Well, looks like it's gettin' light. We better go before all de rabbits goes to bed."

The little boy put one of the biscuits in his jacket pocket and gulped down his coffee. "Let's go, Gus. Where's your gun?"

"Ain't got no gun, boy, don't need one. I gots dese here brickbats. They'll bring home all de rabbits we needs."

"Brickbats? What good are brickbats?"

"Never you mind, boy. Let's go."

"Okay, Gus."

They walked around the barn and down the fence row to get to the ditch. The little boy was half walking and half running to keep up. Pretty soon they reached the ditch, which was totally overgrown with honeysuckle, briars, and sassafras.

"Okay, boy, you hush now. Don' say nothin', and you walk quiet, too, you hear?"

Gus started into the bramble with the little boy trailing behind. He walked quietly, almost sneaking along. The little boy copied every step Gus made, trying not to make a sound.

They hadn't moved far along the ditch when Gus whispered, "Yonder sets Mr. Rabbit, right der. You see him, boy?"

"No."

"Right der under dat tussock, right on the cusp of the ditch. You see dat little black ball, das his eye. He watchin' us."

"No, Gus, I don see no eye."

"Okay, well, we goin' get Brer Rabbit." Gus took a brickbat out of his overall coat and pitched it right at the rabbit. All the little boy could see was dust where the brickbat had torn through the bushes.

"Okay, boy, now's your job; you scamper down en de ditch and fetch me dat rabbit. And get my brickbat, too. Hits a good one."

The little boy stumbled through the honeysuckle and got the rabbit. He could not believe what he had just seen. "Man, you killed this rabbit with a brickbat! How'd you do that, Gus? Can't nobody hit a rabbit on the head with a brickbat!"

"Well, I did, but first you gots to see de rabbit. Come on now, be quiet, you hear?"

The old black man and the little curly-headed white boy continued creeping down the ditch bank, but there were no more rabbits that day.

They went by the little boy's home where they showed the rabbit to his mama. She could not believe that Gus had killed it with a brickbat.

Gus left the little boy with his mama and went home with his rabbit.

Breshin'

The little boy was down at Gus Fairley's place, helping him put up the mules.

"Boy, you tell Miss Mary Lee's boys and Joe that we's goin' breshin' tonite. Tell 'em to meet me at the big barn 'bout dus' dark. You do dat for me?"

"Yessa, Mr. Gus. I'll run down there right now. What'ya mean breshin'?"

"Don' you worry non' 'bout dat. You an' dem boys meet me at de big barn." One o' you bring a tow sack and ast Joe if Uncle Jim got a couple of light'r 'knots; could we please borrow two?"

"Breshin', two lighter knots and one tow sack, got it! Meet you at dusk dark at the big barn! I'll run down to Miss Mary Lee's right now and tell the boys."

Right about the time when it was just starting to get a little dark, but you could still see red streaks in the sky, all of the boys in the neighborhood began to gather around the big barn that housed all of the farm's mules. Somehow the word had gotten around. Besides Joe, Uncle Jim's youngest son, and Miss Mary Lee's boys, there were several others. Of course, Gus's two younger boys, Brother-Boy and William, were there, but also some boys who lived off the Old Maxton Road. Miss Hattie Brown's grandson, Old Soul, and his friend, Paint, had come; so had Joe's older brother, Jessie Lewis. He came along, although he was quite a bit older than the rest of the boys.

The little curly-headed boy was the only white boy in the crowd.

Everybody was laughing and horsing around, throwing dirt clods and even dried mule apples at each other. Several were trying to knock down a big wasps' nest up under the eave of the barn roof.

Gus came around the end of the barn, laughing and joking with everybody, but checking all the while to see if everybody had what they needed.

"Yep, plenty o' boys and lighter 'knots and a poke. Wid dis many boys we'll need two. Brother-Boy, run to de house and fetch another sack. Boys, couple o' you take dis here axe and go lop some o' dem low-hangin' lim's off dat wile cherry yonder. We'll need 'bout eight or six o''em. Lookie here, dey needs to be 'bout three feet long and thick wid twigs and leaves."

Several of the boys went and collected the limbs.

"Well, it's gettin' dark enough 'bout now. Le's go." And off they went.

"We goin' firs' to de big ditch, and I'll tell you boys what we goin' do when we gets der."

When they got to the ditch, Gus divided the boys into two groups, one on each side of the ditch. He handed the oldest boy in each group a burning lighter knot and gave two others one of the limbs each.

"Okay, now. I wants de man wid de light'r 'knot to walk down side o' de ditch right slow-like ahold'n dat light as high as you can. An' de two other mens wid de breshes you slips alon' en front o' de light. De idea is dat when de light shines down in de briars an' brambles, de li'l birds and sparrers dats sleepin' down in der will flush out an' flutter up through the thicket. Dats de time dat de boys wid de breshes do der work. When de birds flutters up thru de thick, swat 'em down wid dem breshes, knock em down."

"Some o' you other boys scrambl' 'round and catch dem knocked down birds an' pop dey heads off and throw 'em in yo sack. Lookie here now, you boys take turns now, der's plenty work ahead, so's everybody be tired 'for we's through. You boys work together!"

Everybody was excited, and the two groups started down the ditch on opposite sides. It didn't take long before everybody knew exactly what to do, and after trudging up and down all of the ditches on the farm, the tow sacks were getting full. They had English sparrows, thrashers, wood thrushes, cardinals, tomtits, and other birds that were probably some kind of finches.

The boys had hunted all of the ditch banks and wood's edges. Everybody was getting tired. Gus had the boys gather up dried limbs, weeds, and dried grass. They built a bonfire and started cleaning the little birds by pulling feathers and "swinshin" the down over the open flames. They cooked the birds on pointed sticks held over the coals. Every boy got full, and they all lay on the ground around the fire and listened to Gus, telling stories about the stars.

It was not until years later that the little curly-headed boy learned it was bad to kill songbirds.

Peddlin'

The little curly-headed boy woke up and quickly remembered that he had a lot of work to do today. "Will's going to dig 'taters today, and I'm going to help him."

He looked for his overalls but could not find them anywhere. He knew he had dropped them the night before right there on the floor. "Mama must have put them in the dirty clothes basket. Ain't no sense in putting on clean clothes when you got to do dirty work."

He went to the dirty clothes hamper out in the hall, pulled his old overalls out, took off his pajamas, and threw them in the basket. After he had put on his overalls he went downstairs.

Mama was already in the kitchen getting ready to cook breakfast.

"Mornin', Mama. We are goin' to dig 'taters today, and Will says we're going to peddle them in town. I'm goin' to see if Will is already milking ol' Bessie."

"Don't you want some breakfast, honey? Did you get those old dirty pants out of the dirty clothes hamper? What's wrong with you, boy? If I live to be five thousand years old, I don't think I'll ever understand you! Why are you putting on old clothes? Those old things smell awful!"

"Aw, Mama, we're going to dig 'taters today, and I'll be crawling 'round in the dirt. I don't need to wear clean clothes. I'm going to check on Will; I'll be right back to eat something."

The little boy darted out the back door, leaped down the steps, and ran toward the barn. Cotton came running after him, jumping up at the little boy's hands, as they ran along. "Morning, Cotton, you a good dog? How you doing this morning? You going help me pick 'taters today? I bet you ain't. I bet you're goin' rat hunting in the 'tater vines."

He and Cotton tore into the barn where Will was milking ol' Bessie. Just like always, when they came bursting into the milk room, ol' Bessie was startled and started stomping her feet. Will had to jerk the milk pail out from under her and calm her down.

"Boy, it looks like you could walk some'ers 'stead o' runnin' everywhere. Whyn't you slow down sometime? You 'bout scared ol' Bessie to deff. Dadblam'it, she done kick some mud off'n her foots into de milk. I gots to throw hit away now. It's good dat I's jes started, 'stead of finished. What you in sech a hurry for anyhow?"

"Will, I'm sorry I scared ol' Bessie. I'm just excited about diggin' 'taters! We're goin' to dig 'taters, ain't we?"

"What de debil you excited 'bout work'n for? Boy, is you crazy? Hit's jes work!"

"I know, Will, but I don't ever get to do no real work. I want to help with the 'taters. I can pick 'em up and put 'em in a basket's good as anybody. Besides that, you said we're goin' peddle them in town."

"Shore you can and shore we are. We'll get us some o' dem big ol' pears, too. Dem ladies in town loves to buy pears."

"Man-o-man, I can climb the tree and pick the pears and toss 'em down to you! Won't have to shake 'em out and bruise them. You let me pick them, won't you, Will?"

"Shore, das de bes' way, and I shore can't clim' no tree like you can. I ain't never seed nobody natural up in a tree like you is. You pretty near a monkey, you is."

"Yeah, I can climb pretty good. I ain't scared o' climbing."

"Well, you go on back to de house and eat you some breakus an' I'll finish milkin' ol' Bessie."

After a while, the little boy had finished eating his breakfast and his mama had gotten tired of fussing about his dirty old coveralls. Will was through milking and had caught up Maude. He was heading toward the sweet potato patch with the turning plow when the little boy caught up with him.

The little curly-head picked up potatoes all day long. He sure never knew that there were so many potatoes in the world. Man, was he tired.

His knees were sore, his arms were tired, and his back hurt like fire. He stood up and stretched his back, saying, "Oh Lordy, Trussy caught a cramp!"

Will laughed at him. "Boy, you jes thinks yo back hurts. You ain't got no back, hit's jes grizzl'. You waits till you gets to my age 'fore yo back hurts."

"I hope I don't ever see another 'tater. How many bushels we got, Will? I know we got ten, but I don't know how many more there are."

Will laughed again. "You put me to de mind of de feller what couldn't count pas' twelve and was countin' pigs. He said der was twelve pigs and another one what was runnin' around too fast to count."

"Aw, Will, how many we got?"

"I believe we gots eighteen, das what I believes. Der is ten bushels and yonder is eight more and dat comes to eighteen. That many, with the pears we goin' pick in de mornin', goin' be a full wagon load."

In the morning after milking, Will and the little curly-headed boy collected the big, hard cooking pears.

The little boy scampered up the old pear tree. It was easy. The trunk was knurly and had big old lumps all over it, and the little boy just about walked right up the tree. It was huge, and the limbs were large and easy to walk out on. He started picking pears and tossed them down to Will.

Finally, the little curly-headed boy reached the top of the tree and was through picking. He could see that Will had filled up six or seven bushels of pears. "Man-o-man, we're goin' to make some money today!"

Will went to the barn lot, hitched Maude to the wagon, and loaded the sweet potatoes. He pulled around to pick up the pears.

"Run, go tell yo mama dat we's leavin' an' will be back late dis evening. Don' get no lunch 'cause we's goin' buy us some o' dem sardines and sodie crackers and a big ol' Nehi orange drink. Meet you at the back gate."

"Bye, Mama, we're getting ready to leave!" shouted the little boy, as he was rushing into the kitchen, slamming the screen door behind him.

"You enjoy yourself, you sweet darling child. I love you. You better mind Mr. Will and keep yourself out of mischief. Come, give me a hug."

"Aw, Mama!"

The little boy ran as fast as he could to where Will was waiting. He climbed up the front wheel to sit beside Will on the high cross board that was the seat. He felt like a giant sitting up so high. He looked back to survey the load and was pleased.

All the way to town, the little boy asked Will a thousand questions. "Why are mules' ears so long? Why did a goat stink so bad? What was a singletree? What was a clevis? Why did a chicken molt? Why did they call that thing in the middle of a horse's hoof a frog? Why . . . ?"

Will knew the answer to all of these questions, but mostly just answered with a grunt and "'cause." When the boy asked Will why he was black, Will told him it was from drinking too much coffee and from chewing too much tobacco.

It was mid-morning when they turned off the old Maxton Road onto Caldonia Street. Will pulled Maude off the dirt road and led her to a chinaberry tree to let her rest in the shade for a while.

The little boy took in all the scenery. Caldonia was a steep, red-clay and rutted street, lined both sides with shotgun houses close together. All of the narrow houses had front porches with broken-down straight-back

chairs on most of them. Every home had a small garden, an outhouse, and a woodpile at the very back of the narrow lot.

The houses were heated with wood, and even in hot weather there was the smell of wood smoke in the air from wood-fired kitchen stoves. There was also the smell of rabbit hutches, chicken coops, and outhouses.

Old men, too old or too broken down to work, were sitting on the porches or walking in the street. From time to time there were old yellow dogs asleep in the street, a female dog with pups sniffing about some trash, and chickens scratching up bugs.

Will clucked old Maude to a start and directed her up the hill. He began chanting, "Pears and 'taters, 'taters and pears, come get yo' 'taters, come get yo' pears!" The little boy was excited; he could hear screen doors slamming and see women coming out of front doors.

Each woman came to the wagon with her own lard tin or a peck basket. The little boy helped the women fill their containers, and they paid Will. The pair worked their way slowly up the street, stopping and starting, filling up containers, taking in money, and laughing and talking with the women. Will knew all of them by name, and the little boy enjoyed hearing Will chide and tease them.

Will pulled Maude into the yard of a store on the corner where Caldonia joined McGirts Bridge Road. He stopped the wagon, got down, and went into the store. The little boy sat on the back of the wagon with only a few potatoes left. They had sold almost an entire wagon load in a very short distance. You could still see the bottom of the hill where they had started earlier in the day.

Will returned with sardines, soda crackers, and two tall Nehi orange drinks. The little boy was thrilled; he had never eaten lunch off the back of a wagon before, and this was a real treat for him.

Somehow the rest of the potatoes were sold, and the little curly-headed boy suddenly got really tired. He put his head in the old man's lap and fell sound asleep.

When they got home, Will armed up the little boy, carried him to the kitchen door, and passed him to his mama. "Miss Stella, dis youngen shore is tared. Yes'm, dat lil' ol' boy is right tuckered out, but I 'speck dat you goin' hear some stories 'bout dis day."

Camping

Douglas Grubbs and the little curly-headed boy — after he had grown up some and wasn't such a little boy — decided that they would go camping. School had let out for the summer and both boys were getting a little bit tired of doing nothing. They decided to go camping.

Douglas lived about a mile up the railroad going toward town. He was the little boy's closest "white boy" neighbor, and they had gotten to be real close friends at school. Oftentimes Douglas would leave home and walk to the little boy's house early in the morning, and they would fool around most of the day shooting robins and mockingbirds with their air rifles.

Douglas was a real good shot with a BB gun. His daddy had taught him to shoot from the hip, and most times he could hit a thrown-up tin can several times before it hit the ground. Douglas had a lever-action Daisy air rifle, and he could put shots in a target one after the other, really fast. The little boy's gun wasn't so good; he had a single-shot and had to load each BB into the end of the barrel before each shot. They got tired of shooting BBs and decided that they would go camping the next week.

Douglas showed up about 7 o'clock the next Monday morning with his air rifle and a fishing pole. The little boy had collected everything they both would need. They did not need much. They were going to live off the land.

The little boy got his mama's thin metal frying pan, some hog lard, salt, coffee, some cornmeal, and two metal cups. This would be all they needed after fishing and hunting. Douglas brought an old hatchet, a used shower curtain, and some hay bailing twine. This would make a good tent. The two boys packed their stuff in two old flour sacks, said good-bye to the little boy's mama, and started off walking to Harry Malloy's pond. They planned to be gone for a week.

Harry Malloy's pond was a really old cypress tree-filled pond about two miles down a dirt lane directly in front of the little boy's house. The pond had been built way back—probably around the turn of the century, around 1900, maybe even before the Civil War—the branch head being between the old Covington farm and the Malloy farm near the old Stewartsville cemetery.

The McNairs owned the Covington farm and did not let just anybody fish in Malloy's pond, but Mr. Harry Malloy was the little boy's kinfolk, so he had a right to fish in it all he wanted. Very few people tried to fish Malloy pond because they could not get past John Shep.

John Shep McCoy was an old black man who was the caretaker for the pond and farmed the land for the McNairs. To get to the pond, everybody had to go through Shep's side yard.

Douglas Grubbs and the little boy stopped at Shep's house where they saw him on the back porch.

"You boys looks like you goin' fish'n. How you, Mister Jimmy? How you doin' t'day"?

"Yessir, Mister John Shep, my friend and I goin' camping over 'cross the pond over there on Mister Harry Malloy's pine thicket. We thought maybe we'd catch us some fish to eat and cook us up some. We goin' shoot us some sparrows to cook over a campfire."

"You is? You ain't brought nuth'n to eat with you? Camp'n, you goin' camp'n?"

"We got us some cornmeal and lard. We goin' to cook us some cornbread to eat with the fish."

"Well, glory, now dat sound lik' fun. You plannin' to stay dere a while, is you?"

"Yessir, Mister John Shep, we plannin' to stay a whole week."

"A week? Where you boys goin' sleep? You can stay under de picknic shed if you want. Probably won't be nobody to bother you, ain't no Bar-b-ques goin' be dis week. Don't hardly be no folks aroun' a'tall."

"Nawsir, we got us a old plastic sheet we goin' put up for a tent, and each of us got an ol' army blanket. We goin' make us a camp up the hill in them pine trees over yonder."

"Well, I never! Shore do hope you boys don' starve to deff."

"Naw, we'll be awright. Mr. Shep. Don't you worry none 'bout us. We'll be alright."

"Well, shaw, you boys have fun now."

The little boy and his friend grabbed up their sacks and hiked them across their shoulders, got their fishing poles and guns, and headed to the pond.

Just past Miss Ina's lodge, there was a wild plum thicket. "Sure do hope them plums get ripe this week. They're awful good, specially them yellow ones yonder."

Everything on the right side of the lane was grown up with vines, brambles, wild cherries, and such. No one had used Miss Ina McNair's lodge in years. It was built during the Roaring Twenties for a party place and a dance hall for Miss Ina and her wealthy friends.

The lodge had once been a beautiful place with magnificent cypress paneling and French doors that went from the floor to the ceiling all along both the front and the back sides. These doors could all be opened, allowing cool evening breezes to flow through. When all the doors were opened it gave people a real sense of freedom and openness. They would dance right on out into the backyard onto a brick patio. In the winter when the weather was bad and all the doors were closed, two huge fireplaces on opposite ends of the dance floor could be put to use.

The little boy never went near Miss Ina's lodge. Somehow he knew he would get into trouble if he ever bothered the place. He never really wanted to go near it anyway; he just always came this way to go fishing.

Douglas and the little curly-headed boy made a camp putting up the shower curtain across a ridge pole and tying everything down with baling twine. They carried in armloads of pine straw and made deep beds of straw under the cover, threw in their blankets, and were ready.

"Let's go find us some fishing worms and go catch us some supper."

"Awright."

Douglas grabbed up the hatchet, and the two boys got their poles and hiked toward the pond. "There ought to be some bait down there below the dam. Yonder is an old rotten log; ought to be some grub worms under all that mess."

The boys found some wrigglers and a few white grubs and baited up their hooks. They fished all day and didn't catch anything. They fished in the race below the spillway, off the dam, all along the edge in the shallows and the lily pads, and off the pier. They didn't catch anything.

Late in the evening they ambled back to camp, and the little curly-headed boy mixed up some cornmeal, salt, and water to fry out some corn pones. Douglas got a good fire going, and the two boys lounged around the fire cooking up some corn bread. That, plus some coffee, was all they had to eat that day, but it was awful good to them.

"Maybe tomorrow we'll catch us some fish to eat."

"Sure do hope so."

On the third or fourth day, after eating nothing but a few green plums and some cornbread, the two boys were getting somewhat weak.

"I sure do feel bad. I can hardly lift my feet up when I walk. Man, I hope we catch us something. I believe I could eat a muskrat."

"Man, I would eat anything 'cept more of them green plums. I had some kind of awful bellyache. I ain't goin' eat no more of them things."

About that time they saw John Shep pedaling a boat back toward the boathouse from up in the pond. They hadn't even known that Shep was in there fishing.

Shep saw the boys and waved.

"How you boys doin'? Catching many fish?"

The little curly-headed boy and his friend could not help but notice that Shep had a string of juicy-looking fish. They sure looked good.

Shep grinned to himself when he noticed the boys' stares. He'd been keeping an eye on the two now and then without them knowing it. He also knew that their fishing luck hadn't been too good.

"Ah hope you boys don' mind iffn I cooks up a few fish here at yo' fire. You all wants to join me, o' have you done et?"

The little boys just about fell over themselves grabbing the frying pan and getting the fire started. They were proud to offer Shep some coffee, and the little curly-headed boy fixed it himself, nice and strong, just the way his mama liked it.

The boys sat there, their eyes glued to the fish as it sizzled and hissed over the fire. They were so hungry by now that it was hard not to snatch the hot fish right out of the pan when Shep said it was ready.

"Man, that sure was good," Douglas said, and both boys wished there was more. All the fish disappeared in no time, with Shep barely getting any for himself.

Shep saw how hungry the boys were, and figured they'd had just about enough camping time.

"Looks lak there's a storm comin'," Shep remarked, looking up at the sky. There might have been a cloud or two passing by, but the two boys didn't even look. They were *really* ready to go home.

"I reckon," said the little curly-headed boy, "maybe we oughta head home. Can we walk with you?"

"Shore can," smiled Shep. "I hep you pack up yo' stuff."